This book belongs to

....

Detective Adventure and Other Stories

How this collection works

This *Biff, Chip and Kipper* collection is one of a series of four books at **Read with Oxford Stage 4**. It contains four stories: *Two Left Feet, May Morning, The Portrait Problem* and *Detective Adventure*. These stories will help to broaden your child's wider reading experience. There are also fun activities to enjoy throughout the book.

How to use this book

Find a time to read with your child when they are not too tired and are happy to concentrate for about fifteen to twenty minutes. Reading with your child should be a shared and enjoyable experience. It is best to choose just one of the stories for each session.

For each story, there are tips for reading the story together. At the end of each story you will find four 'Talk about the story' questions. These will help your child to think about what they have read, and to relate the story to their own experiences. The questions are followed by a fun activity.

Enjoy sharing the stories!

Contents

Two Left Feet 5

May Morning 33

The Portrait Problem 61

Detective Adventure 97

Authors and illustrators

Two Left Feet written by Roderick Hunt, illustrated by Alex Brychta

May Morning written by Roderick Hunt, illustrated by Nick Schon

The Portrait Problem written by Roderick Hunt, illustrated by Alex Brychta

Detective Adventure written by Roderick Hunt, illustrated by Nick Schon

OXFORD
UNIVERSITY PRESS

Great Clarendon Street, Oxford, OX2 6DP, United Kingdom

Oxford University Press is a department of the University of Oxford. It furthers the University's objective of excellence in research, scholarship, and education by publishing worldwide. Oxford is a registered trade mark of Oxford University Press in the UK and in certain other countries

Two Left Feet, May Morning, The Portrait Problem, Detective Adventure first published in 2015
This Edition published in 2018

British Library Cataloguing in Publication Data
Data available

ISBN: 978-0-19-276427-0

10 9 8 7 6 5 4 3 2 1

Paper used in the production of this book is a natural, recyclable product made from wood grown in sustainable forests. The manufacturing process conforms to the environmental regulations of the country of origin.

Printed in China

Acknowledgements

Series Editor: Annemarie Young
Additional artwork by Stuart Trotter

Tips for reading *Two Left Feet*

Children learn best when reading is relaxed and enjoyable.

- Talk about the title and the picture on page 6. Then read the speech bubble.
- Discuss what you think the story might be about. Explain that the expression 'two left feet' means someone is not a good dancer.
- Share the story, encouraging your child to read as much of it as they can.
- Give lots of praise as your child reads and help them when necessary.
- If your child gets stuck on a word that is decodable, encourage them to say the sounds and then blend them together to read the word. Read the whole sentence again. Focus on the meaning.
- If the word is not decodable, or is still too tricky, just read the word for them, re-read the sentence and move on.
- When you've finished reading the story, talk about it with your child, using the 'Talk about the story' questions at the end. Then do the activity.

Children enjoy re-reading stories, and this helps to build their confidence.

Have fun!

For more activities, free eBooks and practical advice to help your child progress with reading visit **oxfordowl.co.uk**

Two Left Feet

"It's that time of year, again," said Mum. She turned the television on.

"Oh no! It's not that dance show again," moaned Kipper.

The children sat with Mum and Dad.

"It's funny," said Mum. "You always moan and groan. Then you enjoy the show as much as we do."

Dad liked the show. It was a contest for people who had never danced before. They had to learn how.

Later, Biff saw Dad in the kitchen. He was pretending to dance with the mop.

"Dad!" said Biff. "You are funny."

“Well, I wish I was good at dancing, but I have two left feet,” said Dad.

“What do you mean?” asked Biff.

“Ask Mum,” said Dad.

In town, Biff saw a poster. It was about a dance competition.

"Why don't you and Dad go in for it?" she asked.

“Ha-ha!” said Mum. “Have you seen Dad dance? He has two left feet.”

“What do you mean?” asked Biff.

“He’s a hopeless dancer,” said Mum.

Biff and Chip spoke to Gran. Biff showed her a leaflet about the dance competition.

"Dad says he wants to dance, but he has two left feet," said Chip.

"Maybe you can teach him, Gran," said Biff. "You are a good dancer."

Every Monday evening Mum went out. As soon as she had left, Gran came to the house.

Biff and Chip cleared a space in the kitchen.
“What’s going on?” asked Dad.
“Let’s go dancing!” said Gran.

Dad and Gran began to dance.

"Poor Dad," said Chip. "I see why Mum says he has two left feet."

"I'm sorry about your toe, Gran," said Dad. "I'll *never* learn to dance."

"Rubbish," said Gran. "We just need to work hard, that's all."

Dad practised his steps. But he only did it when Mum was out.

"He's getting better," said Chip.

Soon Dad had learned the steps.
He began to enjoy Gran's lessons.

"It's time to enter Dad and Mum in the dancing competition!" said Chip.

The children had a surprise for Mum. Chip had cut a big foot out of card.

"What on earth is it?" asked Mum.

"One of Dad's left feet," said Kipper.

Dad whirled Mum round the kitchen.

"Let's go dancing," he said.

"Goodness me," gasped Mum. "Dad can dance after all."

Mum and Dad wanted to win the competition. They had dancing lessons to make them even better.

"We need to work hard," said Mum.

Mum and Dad were ready for the competition.

"Wow!" said Kipper. "You look really good in that."

Gran and the children were excited when Dad and Mum danced in the competition.

Then Dad bumped into a chair.

"Oh no!" said Chip. "I hope Dad hasn't got his two left feet back!"

"Go on, Dad," called Biff. "You can win. I'm sure you can."

Dad and Mum were soon dancing well again.

"They look great," said Kipper. "I do hope they win."

It was time for the judge to call out the winners of the competition.

Kipper held his breath. Biff crossed her fingers.

Mum and Dad came third in the competition. They won a little goblet made of crystal.

"It was worth a sore toe," said Gran.

Talk about the story

Why do you think the expression 'two left feet' means someone isn't a good dancer?

How does Dad's dancing improve?

Why does Gran say it was worth a sore toe?

What do you enjoy doing now that you weren't very good at to begin with?

Who wins the cup?

Each square has the hidden name of a dance.

They are RUMBA TANGO WALTZ and SAMBA.

Which dance leads to the gold cup in the middle?

T	R	Y	U	P
A	D	L	Y	S
N	U	E	X	I
G	V	K	T	F
O	H	K	D	S

P	L	R	N	R
B	C	I	U	L
Q	T	M	J	K
R	B	G	C	T
A	C	L	H	N

S	U	Y	G	D
H	A	F	C	M
U	I	M	R	G
Y	K	S	B	N
V	O	G	L	A

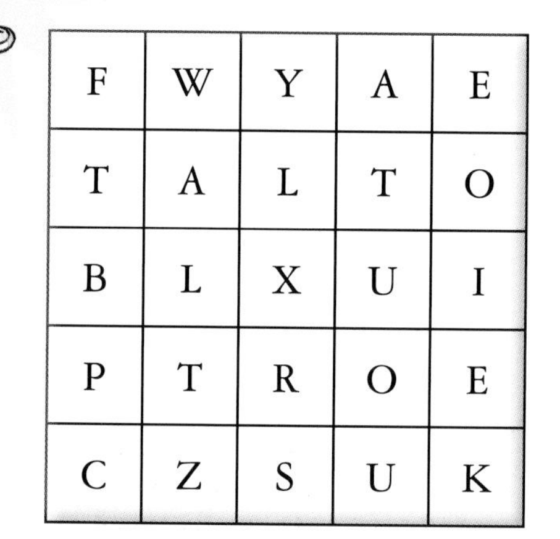

F	W	Y	A	E
T	A	L	T	O
B	L	X	U	I
P	T	R	O	E
C	Z	S	U	K

Tips for reading *May Morning*

Children learn best when reading is relaxed and enjoyable.

- Talk about the title and the picture on page 34. Then read the speech bubble.
- Discuss what you think the story might be about. If your child isn't familiar with May Day, explain that it's a festival celebrating the arrival of spring on the 1st of May.
- Share the story, encouraging your child to read as much of it as they can.
- Give lots of praise as your child reads, and help them when necessary.
- If your child gets stuck on a word that is decodable, encourage them to say the sounds and then blend them together to read the word. Read the whole sentence again. Focus on the meaning.
- If the word is not decodable, or is still too tricky, just read the word for them, re-read the sentence and move on.
- When you've finished reading the story, talk about it with your child, using the 'Talk about the story' questions at the end. Then do the activity.

Children enjoy re-reading stories, and this helps to build their confidence.

May Morning

What might spoil the maypole dance? Can Mrs May save the day?

Mrs May took the children on to the playing field.

"Why are we going outside, Mrs May?" asked Wilf.

There was a tall pole standing in the playing field. It had ribbons hanging down from the top.

"What is it, Mrs May?" asked Chip.

"It's a maypole," said Mrs May. "I'm going to teach you the maypole dance."

“I want you all to stand in a circle.” Mrs May went on. “Now take hold of a ribbon. Then take four steps backwards.”

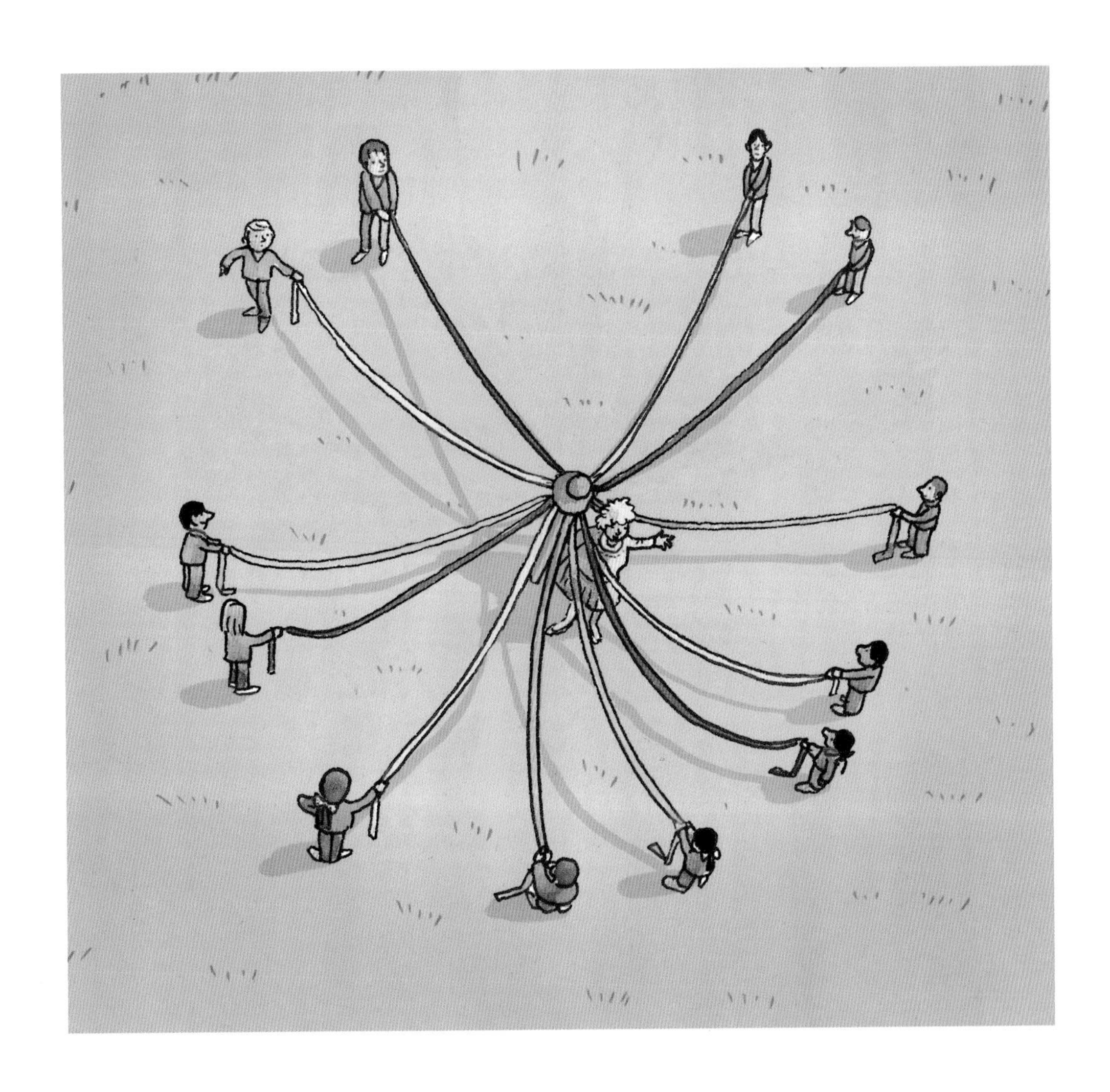

The ribbons spread out in a circle of blue, green, red and yellow colours.

"The dance is quite easy, but we'll walk it first," said Mrs May.

She told them to walk in a circle so the ribbons wound round the pole.

"Now we'll do it to music," she said.

"The pole looks great," said Nadim, "and all we did was walk round it."

"In time, we will learn how to weave a pattern," smiled Mrs May.

"May Day is a special day," said Mrs May. "Who can tell me why?"

"It celebrates Spring," said Wilf.

"And better weather," said Chip.

“It will be fun to celebrate May Day,” said Mrs May. “We are going to have a school fair. Every class is taking part.”

There was a lot to do to prepare for May Morning. Some children were going to sing a song.

The children in Wilma's class painted big pictures of birds and flowers to go round the playground wall.

Mrs May's class worked hard at the maypole dance. They had to remember which way to skip with the ribbons round the maypole.

Two children were chosen to be King and Queen of the May.

"Her dress is nice," said Biff. "But I'm glad I don't have to wear it."

At last it was May Morning, but it was teeming with rain.

The pictures on the playground wall were soaked.

The maypole was standing in a pool of water.
“We can’t dance round that,” said Chip.

"It's going to rain all day," said Nadim's mum. "It's such a shame."

"We will have to celebrate May Morning indoors," said Mrs May.

"But what about the maypole dance?" asked Biff.

"Cheer up! We can still do it," said Mrs May. "Leave it to me."

"We will do the maypole dance in the hall. I'll be the maypole," said Mrs May.

She held up the top of the pole with the ribbons on it.

The children took their places round Mrs May and the music began.

Everyone clapped as the children began to dance.

The ribbons began to weave into a pattern.

The music did not stop, so the children went on dancing.

The pattern went lower.

The ribbons wound round the top of
Mrs May's head.

Everyone cheered at the end.
"So Mrs May saved the day," said Mum.
"That's true," said Nadim's mum.

Mum looked for Dad but he was not in the hall.
“Did you see where Dad went?” asked Mum.

Dad had gone to get a big bunch of flowers for Mrs May.

"Three cheers for Mrs Maypole!" said Dad.

Talk about the story

What happened to the ribbons when the children walked around the maypole at the beginning?

Why was it more difficult when they danced?

What did you think would happen when Mrs May said she'd be the maypole?

What would you do to 'save the day' if it rained on your games at an outdoor party?

Spot the problem

Here is a diagram showing Mrs May's class doing a maypole dance. Each set of footprints is a person. The arrows show the direction of each dancer.

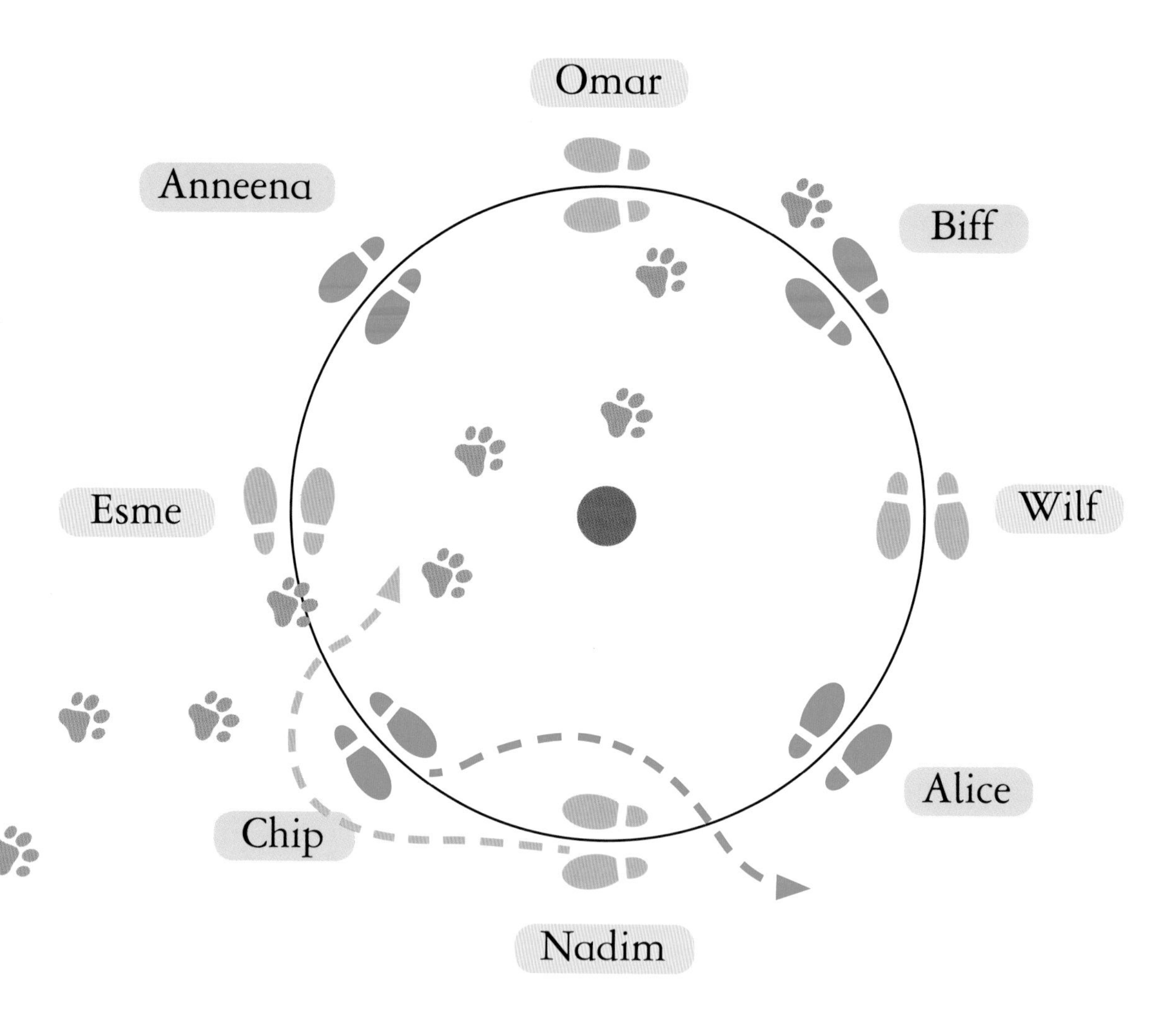

Who is facing the wrong way? Who else is trying to join in the dance?

Tips for reading *The Portrait Problem*

Children learn best when reading is relaxed and enjoyable.

- Talk about the title and the picture on page 62. Then read the speech bubble.
- Discuss what you think the story might be about. You could explain that Botticelli is a famous artist who was born in Florence in 1445.
- Share the story, encouraging your child to read as much of it as they can.
- Give lots of praise as your child reads, and help them when necessary.
- If your child gets stuck on a word that is decodable, encourage them to say the sounds and then blend them together to read the word. Read the whole sentence again. Focus on the meaning.
- If the word is not decodable, or is still too tricky, just read the word for them, re-read the sentence and move on.
- When you've finished reading the story, talk about it with your child, using the 'Talk about the story' questions at the end. Then do the activity.

Children enjoy re-reading stories, and this helps to build their confidence.

The Portrait Problem

The artist Botticelli has a problem. Can the children solve it?

The children in Mrs May's class were painting. They had to do a portrait.

"I want you to paint someone's face," said Mrs May. "First, I will explain how to do it."

Mrs May drew an oval face. She drew three lines across it and put one line down the middle.

"The eyes are halfway down. The top of the ears are level with the eyes," she said.

Chip was good at painting. He had painted a portrait of Anneena.

"It's brilliant," said Nadim. "It looks just like Anneena."

Mrs May put the finished portraits on the wall.

"Mine is rubbish," complained Wilf.

"No it's not," said Biff. "You just haven't got the ears quite right."

Chip had a sketch book. He had done a sketch of Mrs May.

"It's quite good," smiled Mrs May. "To get even better you need to practise. Try to draw as often as you can."

Wilf and Nadim went to play with Chip. Chip's sketch book was in Biff's room. He had done a sketch of Nadim.

"I'd like to be an artist when I grow up," said Chip.

"I'll keep this," said Nadim. "In case you become a famous artist one day!"

Suddenly the magic key began to glow. The magic took the children on a new adventure.

The magic took the children back in time to a city in Italy called Florence.

"I wonder why the key has brought us here," said Chip.

Just then, they heard shouting. A man was at an open window. He was shouting at some men in the street.

"But, sir," called one of the men. "Your picture is too big to go down the stairs."

"We could knock the staircase down," said another man. "But why not just cut six inches off one end of the painting?"

"Impossible!" yelled the man. "I'm sure these children have more sense than you."

He pointed at Wilf, Chip and Nadim.

"Children!" he shouted. "I am Sandro Botticelli, the artist. Come up to my studio and tell me which end to cut off my picture. It has taken me two years to paint it."

"This picture is called 'Spring'," said Sandro. "Do you like it?"

Chip gasped. "It's a famous painting," he whispered. "I've seen it in a book."

Nadim was looking at the window.

"There's no need to take the staircase down," he said. "Knock out the window frame and lower the painting into the street."

"Ha!" said Sandro, clapping his hands. "Bravo! Children often know best."

"You want to be an artist, too?" Sandro asked, looking at Chip's drawings. "You need to work hard and draw all the time. You must look, and study what you see."

“See! I am painting a portrait of a young man,” Sandro went on. “I want you to help me. Put on this tunic so I can copy the folds in it.”

Suddenly there was a loud thumping noise and the house began to shake.

The jars and pots began to rattle. Some fell on to the floor with a crash.

“Is it an earthquake?” gasped Chip.

“Ah!” groaned Sandro. “I cannot work like this. The man next door is a weaver. His looms make the walls shake.”

“Go next door. Please beg him to stop shaking my house,” Sandro pleaded. “He will not listen to me, but maybe he will listen to you.”

The weaver came to the door.

"Your looms are shaking the house of Sandro the artist," said Nadim. "He cannot paint his pictures."

The weaver showed them his looms.

"I weave fine cloth," he said. "It is how I earn my living. And, in my own house, I can do what I please."

"Sandro, the artist, paints beautiful pictures. He paints fine portraits," said Chip. "That is his job."

"Bah! Weaving cloth is a *proper* job," the weaver replied.

“What did he say?” asked Sandro.

“In his own house he can do as he pleases,” said Wilf.

“So!” said Sandro. “I need to teach him a lesson. Wait here.”

Later, Sandro returned with some workmen. They had ropes and long thick poles of wood. On a cart was an enormous stone.

The men built a strong frame. Then they pulled the boulder on to the edge of Sandro's roof.

"Place it on the very edge," Sandro ordered.

"It doesn't look very safe," said Wilf.

Sandro rubbed his hands.

"No. It is not safe," he said. "We will see what happens when the weaver's looms start working."

The weaver's looms began to shake Sandro's house. The enormous stone shook as well. It began to move.

"What are you doing?" cried the weaver. "The stone is unsafe. Remove it!"

"It will fall on to my house. It will crash through my roof," he wailed.

"Well," said Sandro. "In my own house, I can do what I please."

Nadim had an idea. He spoke to the weaver. "Let the artist paint a portrait of you wearing a cloak of your fine cloth. Rich people will see it and want to buy from you."

"Why not work at different times?" Nadim added. "Then you will both be happy."

The two men shook hands. The weaver agreed to work in the mornings. The artist agreed to work in the afternoons.

"That was clever, Nadim," said Wilf.

Sandro began the portrait of the weaver at once. He gave Chip one of his sketches.

Then the magic key began to glow.

“It was funny when the stone on the roof began to shake,” laughed Wilf.

“I wonder if the portrait of the weaver will be in that book I saw at school,” said Chip.

"This is a really good portrait," said Mrs May. "Did you draw it?"

"No, Sandro Botticelli did," said Chip.

"Very funny, Chip!" said Mrs May.

Talk about the story

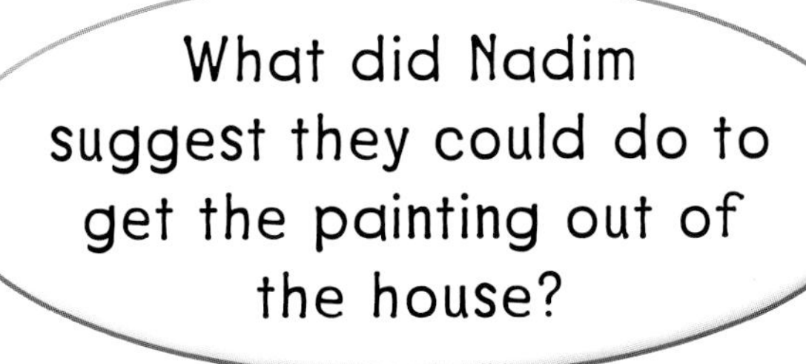

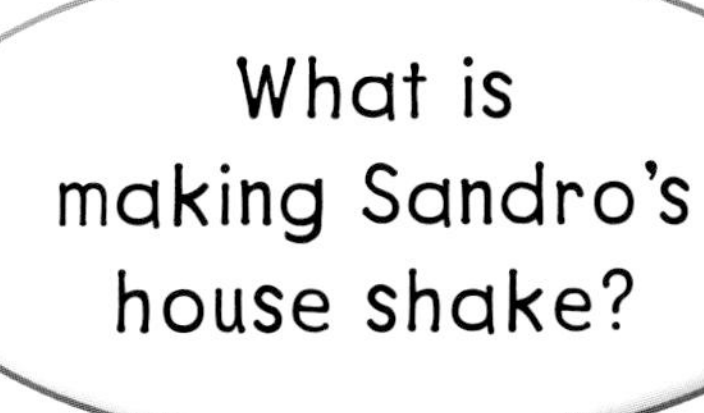

Why did Sandro put the enormous stone on his roof?

Have you ever had to sort out a problem with a friend? How did you do it?

Spot the difference

Picture **A** shows Sandro's studio in the morning.

Picture **B** shows it after the house was shaken.

Find eight differences between the pictures.

Tips for reading *Detective Adventure*

Children learn best when reading is relaxed and enjoyable.

- Talk about the title and the picture on page 98. Then read the speech bubble.
- Discuss what you think the story might be about. Ask if your child has heard of Sherlock Holmes. If not, explain that he's a famous fictional detective from stories written by Arthur Conan Doyle.
- Share the story, encouraging your child to read as much of it as they can.
- Give lots of praise as your child reads, and help them when necessary.
- If your child gets stuck on a word that is decodable, encourage them to say the sounds and then blend them together to read the word. Read the whole sentence again. Focus on the meaning.
- If the word is not decodable, or is still too tricky, just read the word for them, re-read the sentence and move on.
- When you've finished reading the story, talk about it with your child, using the 'Talk about the story' questions at the end. Then do the activity.

Children enjoy re-reading stories, and this helps to build their confidence.

Detective Adventure

It was book week. The children all went as characters from books they had read.

Biff and Chip looked exactly the same.

"Can you tell who we are?" asked Biff.

"I know," said Anneena. "You are the twin detectives in the Tintin books."

"You look good," said Chip, "but who are you?"

"I am Sherlock Holmes, the famous detective," said Anneena. "No crime is too hard for him to solve."

Biff laughed. "Sorry, Anneena. I've never heard of him."

After school Anneena went to play with Biff. She had a book about Sherlock Holmes.

"I love detective stories," Anneena said. "I want to be a detective one day."

Just then, Mum called Biff. "I'm putting the washing machine on," she said.

Biff took a pile of clothes down for Mum to wash. While she was gone, the magic key glowed.

Anneena found herself outside a grand house.

"Oh no!" she said. "I'm not sure I want an adventure by myself."

Suddenly a carriage raced up to the front door. A man jumped out, he had a coat and hat like Anneena's.

"Who are you?" the man demanded.

"I'm a detective," said Anneena.

"You look far too young. When I sent for an assistant, I expected someone older. Well, come on! We have a crime to solve!"

The man ran into the house. A police officer was standing by the door.

"Ah, Mr Holmes," he said. "Inspector Lees is waiting for you."

"The crime took place in the ballroom," said Inspector Lees. "No one has left the room since the theft took place."

"The theft of what?" said Holmes.

"A diamond necklace," the Inspector said.

Two more police officers stood at the door of a large ballroom. A crowd of people were standing inside. A woman was crying.

"Lord and Lady Tuckup are having a party for very rich and famous people," said Inspector Lees. "The Duchess of Almond is here. She *was* wearing her diamond necklace."

"Worth millions, I'm sure," added Holmes.

"At ten o'clock," said Lees, "the lights went out. They came on again almost at once and no one could have left the ballroom. Yet the necklace had been stolen."

“Two of my men were at the door all evening,” the Inspector went on. “No one has been allowed to move from the spot since the robbery took place.”

"Has everyone been searched?" asked Holmes.

"Yes, and we have searched every part of the room," said Lees. "The necklace has not been found. It is a mystery."

"The person who took the necklace must have been standing near the Duchess," said Holmes.

"The maid was standing next to the Duchess," said Lees. "But it couldn't have been her."

"She was holding a huge tray of empty glasses," said Lees.

"I'm *still* holding it!" said the maid. "May I put it down now please? It has been over an hour."

The maid took the tray to a table outside the ballroom. On the way she dropped a glass. Quickly she picked up the broken bits and threw them in a bin.

"Take everyone to the library, Inspector," said Holmes. "Don't let anyone out of your sight. My assistant and I will look for clues. Then we will question each person again."

Anneena and Holmes looked round the empty ballroom.

"Hmm!" said Holmes. "This beats me. No one could have left the ballroom with the necklace. So where is it now?"

Anneena looked round the other room. She peered into the bin with the broken glass. At the bottom was a tennis ball with a split in it.

"How odd to find that!" she said to herself.

In the library, Holmes questioned the maid.

"It was not me, sir," she said. "I was holding a tray of glasses at the time. And I've been searched."

At that moment Anneena ran in. She was holding a tray of glasses.

"Stop!" cried Anneena. "The maid is the thief! Don't let her go."

"She stole the necklace! I know how she did it," Anneena said.

They searched the maid again. The necklace was in her pocket.

"But . . ." gasped the Inspector, "we searched her before. She didn't have the necklace."

"So how *did* she get the necklace out of the room?" asked Holmes.

"In this tennis ball," Anneena said. "She quickly pushed the necklace into the split ball and threw it."

"In the dark, the ball flew over the heads of the police officers. It landed softly in the room behind them. It ended up near the table."

"I see," gasped Holmes. "She dropped the glass so that she could pick the ball up. Then she took the necklace out of the ball and dropped the ball in the bin."

"All the glasses were stuck to the tray except the one that she dropped," said Anneena.

"So she could put the tray down quickly, leaving her hands free to steal the necklace," said Holmes.

The maid began to cry.

"You must have been working with someone who could turn the lights off," Lees said to her. "Who was it?"

"It was the butler," sobbed the maid.

"I did a good job solving this case for you," said Holmes. "I caught the thief."

Anneena looked at Holmes and gasped, but the key began to glow.

"Sorry, Anneena," said Biff, coming back into the room.

"Don't worry," said Anneena. "I've been finding out more about Sherlock Holmes."

Talk about the story

Break the code

Each symbol is a different letter. Break the code by replacing the symbols with letters.

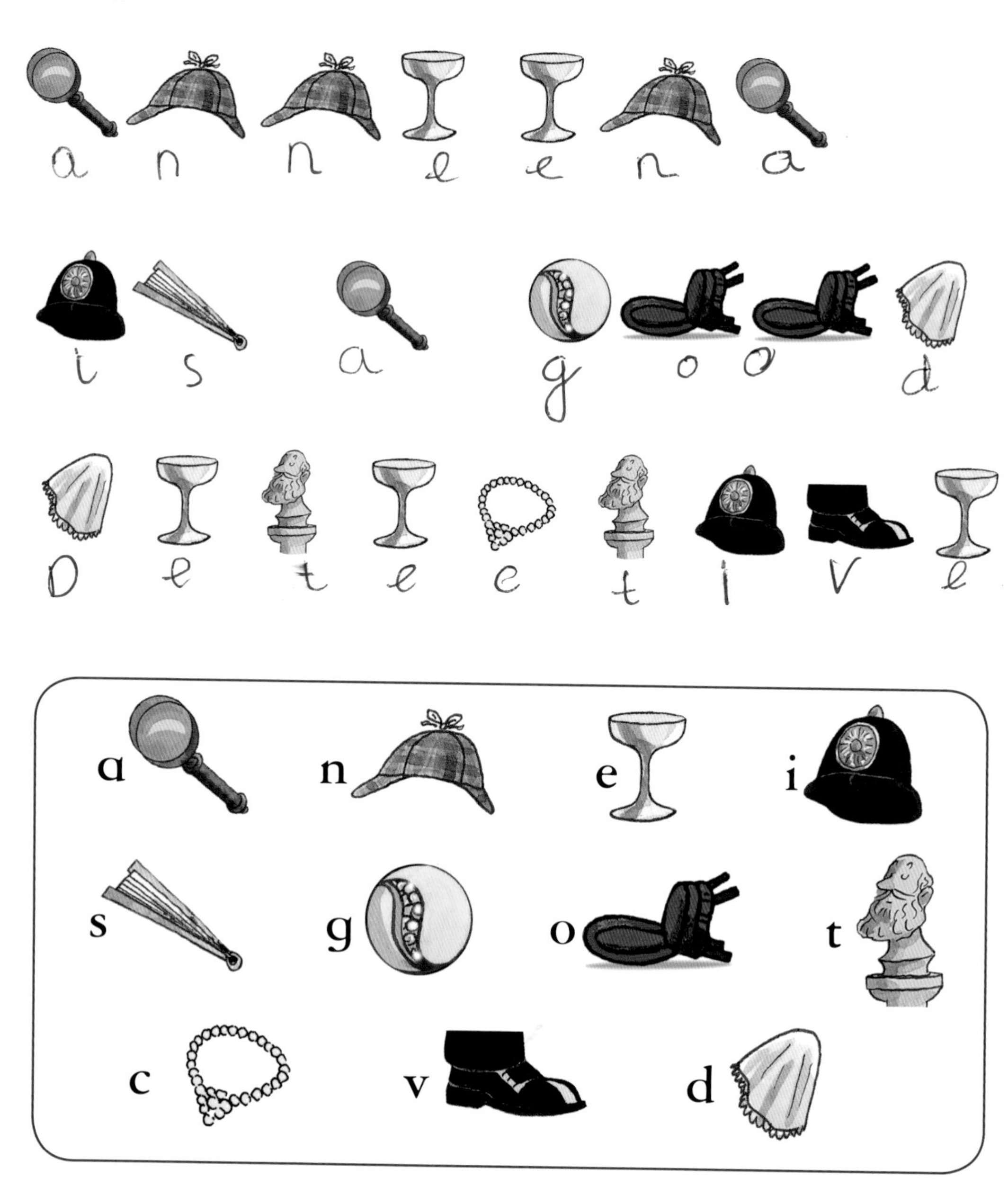

Remembering the stories together

Encourage your child to remember and retell the stories in this book. You could ask questions like these:

- Who are the characters in the story?
- What happens at the beginning of the story?
- What happens next?
- How does the story end?
- What was your favourite part of the story? Why?

Story prompts

When talking to your child about the stories, you could use these more detailed reminders to help them remember the exact sequence of events. Turn the statements below into questions, so that your child can give you the answers. For example, *What do Mum and Dad like watching on TV? What does Dad want to be able to do?* And so on …

Two Left Feet

- Mum and Dad like watching a dancing show on TV.
- Dad wants to be able to dance, so Gran teaches him.
- Mum is very surprised when she finds out that Dad can now dance.
- They enter a dance competition and they do well. They come third!

May Morning

- Biff and Chip are taking part in May Day celebrations at school.
- Mrs May teaches the class how to do a maypole dance.
- But on May Day it's raining, so they have to celebrate inside.
- Mrs May holds the maypole, but is caught up in the ribbons.

The Portrait Problem

- Mrs May is teaching the class about portraits.
- The magic key takes the children back in time to Florence.
- They meet the famous artist, Botticelli, who is having trouble with his neighbour, the weaver.
- The weaver's loom is making Botticelli's studio shake, so Botticelli wants to teach him a lesson.
- He puts a rock on the roof so that it will fall on the weaver's house when the looms shake the house.
- The weaver is cross, but this time the children manage to resolve the dispute.

Detective Adventure

- It's Book Week and Anneena dresses up as the famous detective, Sherlock Holmes.
- Anneena goes on a magic key adventure back to the time of Sherlock Holmes.
- Sherlock Holmes needs her help to solve a crime. A diamond necklace has been stolen.
- They ask lots of questions and Anneena watches everyone carefully.
- Anneena works out what must have happened and explains it to Sherlock Holmes.
- Sherlock Holmes takes the credit for solving the case and Anneena is annoyed, but the magic key takes her back home before she can say anything.

You could now encourage your child to create a 'story map' of each story, drawing and colouring all the key parts of them. This will help them identify the main elements of the stories and learn to create their own stories.